ERR

ERR

DAVID SHRIGLEY

BOOK WORKS

FRONTISPIECE

AN EPLANATION
(OF SORTS, AS FAR AS IS POSSIBLE)

SOME MONTHS AFTER THE FIRST VOLUME WAS
PUBLISHED WE ALL DECIDED TO SIT DOWN
AND HAVE A GOOD LOOK THROUGH IT
(THERE HAD BEEN SOME COMPLAINTS).

WE FOUND:

1. ERRORS IN ~~PRINTING~~ PRINTING (BACK TO FRONT,
(UPSIDE-DOWN ETC.)

2. ERRORS IN ~~TEXT~~ TEXT (MISGUIDED
GENERALISATIONS, GENERAL FALSEHOODS, ETC)

3. ERRORS IN ILLUSTRATIONS (USUAL KIND
OF THING, ETC)

4. MIXED UP THEMES (NOT KNOWING WHAT
YOU'RE TALKING ABOUT, ETC)

5. GENERAL ERRORS (TO DO WITH V.
BASIC THINGS LIKE DIFFERENCE, ETC)

6. ERRORS OF A MORAL KIND (TOO MUCH
EVIL ON ONE PAGE, E.T.C.)

WHAT FOLLOWS IS AN ATTEMPT TO HIGHLIGHT
THESE ERRORS FOR THE BENEFIT OF
THOSE WHO TRIED TO READ THE FIRST
VOLUME. OUR TELEPHONE NUMBER
IS

CONTENTS

INTRODUCT

MOST OF THE PAGES CONTAINED HEREIN ARE ONES WHICH WERE EXCLUDED IN THE FIRST VOLUME ~~██████~~ ~~██████~~ ~~██████~~ E.G. DON'T MAKE SENSE, ~~██████~~ TOO SCARY, ~~██████~~. ~~██████████~~ ~~██████~~ ~~██████████~~ ~~██████~~ CAUSED BY ~~██████████~~ MANY ERRORS THE PAGES FROM THIS VOLUME ARE REMOVED ~~██████~~ ETC , ~~██████~~ IF AND COUPLED WITH THOSE OF THE FIRST VOLUME A SORT OF OVERALL MEANING WILL PREVAIL. THINGS WILL FALL INTO PLACE WE SUGGEST YOU CUT OUT THESE PAGES WITH SCISSORS AND STICK THEM IN WITH CLEAR TAPE (NOT PROVIDED) O.K.?

ALSO

WATERMARK

ALL BOOKS, PAMPHLETS, BROCHURES, CERTIFICATES, ~~██~~ MONEY (NOT COINS) HAVE WATERMARKS TO SHOW ~~██~~ QUALITY + REALNESS. THE WATERMARK HERE IS MISSED OUT. THE WATERMARK CAN BE MADE BY THE READER THRO' PROCESS THUS;

A. EAT LOTS OF FOOD

B. WRITE NAME OF AUTHOR IN SPIT ON EACH PAGE :

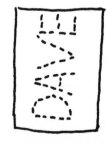

FOREWORD

As you enter the building, please take off you shoes (we shouldn't have to tell you this at this time, you should know by now). Go to reception where Uncle Richard will give you a clean overall (you probably need one by now). Go to the shower and have a good scrub and get togged-up. If anyone asks you where your going just tell them (they'll probably feel sorry for you and let you go on). Head straight for the chamber and bang on the door with your plastic hand (mind the cobwebs). Uncle Richard will be there to give you one of your injections (you'll probably need one by then) and he'll take a bile sample to see ~~strike~~ if the poison we gave you last friday has started to work (we didn't tell you - don't worry). If it has then he will play you punk rock and get you to draw what you hear, like before. If it doesn't work we'll just keep going. You can phone your parents later on but if you tell where you are again we'll cut of your other hand and send that to them - then they'll really know we're serious.

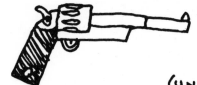

RUSSIAN ROULETTE

5 WAYS TO WIN

1 WAY TO LOSE

(UNDER NORMAL CIRCUMSTANCES)

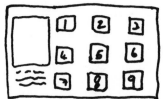

SCRATCHCARD

3 WAYS TO WIN

MYRIAD TO LOSE

DOG FIGHTING

1 WAY TO WIN

1 WAY TO LOSE (APPROX)

NORMAL ROULETTE

99 OR SO OPTIONS

DEPENDS ON HOW MANY YOU TAKE

FRUIT MACHINE

12 WAYS TO WIN

331 WAYS TO LOSE

(OVER 18's)

WATERCOLOUR

ONLY LOSERS

(NOT RECOGNISED BY GOVERNING BODY)

TENNIS

12 WAYS TO WIN (BACKHAND LOB, ETC)

1 TO LOSE (NOT HITTING IT BACK)

(OUTLAWED IN PUBS)

AUTHOR'S NOTE

I AM AN AUTHORITY ON DIRT AND FILTH

I AM AN AUTHORITY ON BAD WEATHER

I AM AN AUTHORITY ON BAD ACCIDENTS

I AM AN AUTHORITY ON WORRIED CHILDREN

I AM AN AUTHORITY ON MEANESS AND CRUELTY

IN FACT I AM AN AUTHORITY ON JUST ABOUT BLOODY ANYTHING YOU CARE TO MENTION......

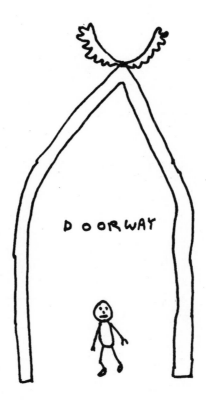

THE I's

I DO NOT KNOW HOW TO WORK A FAX MACHINE
OR A COMPUTER
I DO NOT KNOW ANYONE WITH A MOBILE PHONE
I DO NOT KNOW WHAT THE WORD 'INTERNET' MEANS
I AM UNAWARE OF THE EXISTENCE OF PROTONS
NEUTRONS, ELECTRONS + C.B. RADIO
I HAVE NEVER HEARD THE SUPERIOR SOUND-
QUALITY OF A COMPACT DISC
I OWN A TELEVISION BUT IT DOES NOT HAVE
A REMOTE CONTROL
I ONCE PUT MY CLOTHES IN THE DISHWASHER
I NEED A HEARING AID BUT DO NOT KNOW
WHERE TO BUY ONE
I DO NOT KNOW HOW TO DRIVE A CAR
I HAVE NEVER OPERATED A POWER TOOL
OR A CASSETTE RECORDER
OR A PUSH-BUTTON PHONE
MY FRONT DOOR DOES NOT HAVE A DOORBELL
YOU JUST HAVE TO KNOCK
I DO NOT POSSESS ANY CREDIT CARDS
I AM NOT ALLOWED
WHEN PEOPLE TRY TO TALK TO ME I JUST
GRUNT IN RESPONSE
BUT, SURPRIZINGLY, I AM THE CAPTAIN OF A
V. HIGH-TECH SPACE VESSEL AND AM GOING
ON A MISSION NEXT WEEK. I NEED 12
GOOD MEN. MEN WHO ARE NOT AFRAID OF

$$\frac{2\text{'s}}{2}$$

3's

OLD WOMEN FROM
ANOTHER PLANET

WATER FROM THE PUBLIC
BATHS BOTTLED & SOLD

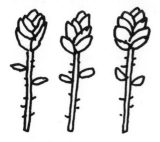

PRICKLY FLOWERS

BUY 2 GET 1 FREE

DEAD UNCLE'S WIG
CUT UP TO MAKE
EYEBROWS + MOUSTACHE

HAND OF OLD WOMAN
MENTIONED EARLIER

DRY FAGS REMAINING
AFTER FLOOD

ME, YOU & YOUR BOYFRIEND

OFFICE FURNITURE

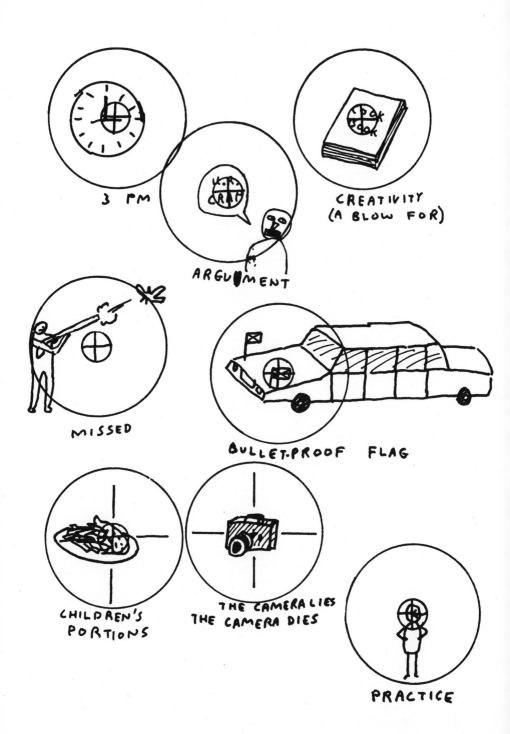

THE TOP OF THE BUILDING ACROSS THE ROAD FROM OUR FLAT IS A SYMBOL OF OUR NEIGHBOURHOOD. IT WAS ONCE GRAND AND CLASSY BUT IS NOW OLD AND COVERED IN BIRD SHIT. THE OTHER DAY I WAS HAVING A BATH AND I THOUGHT I COULD SMELL BURNING. I GOT OUT OF THE BATH AND WENT INTO MY ROOM WHERE THE SMELL WAS EVEN STRONGER. I OPENED A WINDOW TO LET THE SMELL CLEAR. I WONDERED IF I SHOULD GO DOWNSTAIRS TO SEE IF THEY WERE ON FIRE. I DONT GET ON WELL WITH MR. DOWNSTAIRS BECAUSE HE CALLED THE POLICE LAST TIME WE HAD A BAND PRACTICE. EVENTUALLY I CONVINCED MYSELF THAT THE BURNING SMELL WAS GOING AWAY AND I WENT OUT. WHEN ▬▬ ▬ ▬ ▬ ▬▬ ▬▬▬ ▬▬▬ ▬▬▬ ▬▬▬ ▬▬▬ ▬▬ ▬▬ ▬▬ ▬▬ ▬▬ ▬ ▬▬ ▬▬ ▬ ▬▬ ▬.

BODIES OF WATER (IN MY FLAT)

EX - GIRLF

OCEAN OF LOST ADDRESSES
WRITTEN ON SCRAP PAPER
+ BURIED IN →

SEA OF UNEMPTIED BINS
STALE CEREAL + OLD NEWSPAPERS

LAKE OF CAN'T REMEMBER

RERSERVIOIR OF DUST
(IF I COULD SELL IT I WOULD
BE RICH)

RIVER OF NO TOILET PAPER

CANAL OF FEAR OF
GETTING BURGLED

POOL OF J. MONK
+ J. DONACHIE

POND OF NO
LIGHTBULBS

PUDDLE OF SOMETHING

BUCKET OF
CUPBOARD FULL
OF BROKEN
THINGS.

GLASS OF JACKIE'S VODKA
(AFTER SHE'S GONE TO BED)

HERE WE HAVE

2- LEGGED OCTOPUS TALKIN' ON TH' BIG SKELETON
OF THE REINDEER.....

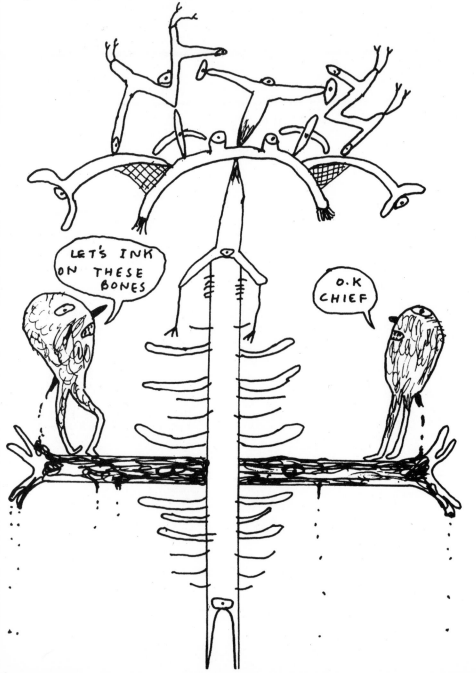

STORY IN PROG.

YOU, MY FRIEND ARE A CIRCLE AND I AM A SQUARE....

NO, I TELL A LIE, YOU ARE A SQUARE AND I AM A CIRCLE, NO, FORGET THAT, YOU ARE A LITTLE MOUSE SCURRYING ACROSS THE WOODLAND FLOOR AND I AM A HUNGRY OWL EYING YOU FROM ABOVE

NO MAYBE I AM THE MOUSE AND YOU ARE THE OWL, NO, YOU ARE A HAWK, A BIG, VICIOUS, HUNGRY, BIG EAGLE OF A HAWK

BUT YOU CAN'T CATCH ME BECAUSE I RUN DOWN A HOLE.

THE YARN

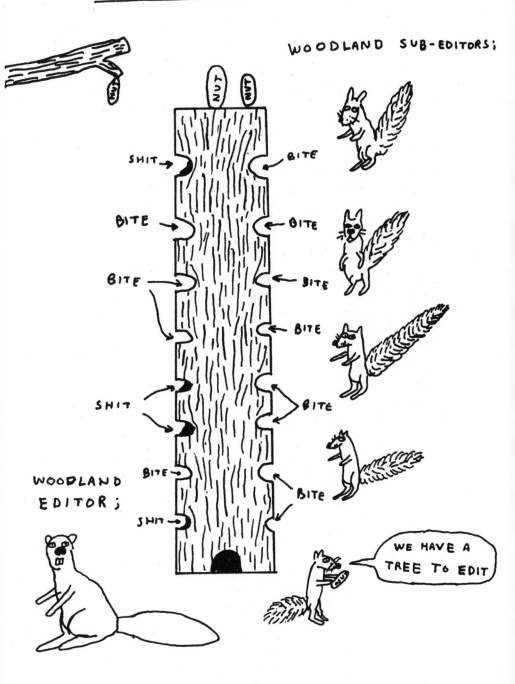

PREFACE

FORK-
LIGHTENING
SEEN
IN
NEGATIVE

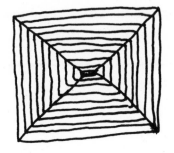

PYRAMID SEEN FROM
THE AIR

THE SKY SEEN
FROM INSIDE
A DRAIN

HAIR
SEEN
UNDER A
MICROSCOPE

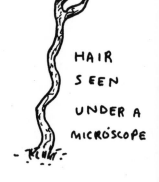

ELEPHANT SEEN IN THE
MIND'S EYE OF PEOPLE IN
OLDEN TIMES HAVING
ONLY HEARD ABOUT THEM

HER EYES SEEN WHEN SEEING
ME AFTER I HAD BEEN AWAY
FOR SUCH A LONG TIME WITHOUT
SAYING WHERE I WAS.

THE PERFECT SPY

FIRST SMALL PARTS
WALK-ONS, MESSENGERS, CROWD-
SCENE, WOMAN IN SHOP, EARLY
CASUALTIES, OFF STAGE SCREAMS,
UN-NAMED CHARACTERS.

NEXT BIGGER ROLES WITH LINES
THE BARMAN, THE DOCTOR,
THE ELDER BROTHER, FIGHT SCENE.

3. PICTURE ON POSTER
BEST SUPPORTING ACTRESS

THEN BIG BLOCKBUSTER
U.R. IT.

N°4 YOU ARE A HOUSEHOLD
NAME EVERYBODY WANTS
TO BE YOU. YOU ARE
HUNTED BY FANS.

ALSO EVERYONE STARTS TO
LOOK LIKE YOU. PRETTY
SOON THE WORLD IS
POPULATED BY YOUR
DOPPLEGANGERS.

AND YOU'RE JUST ONE
OF THE CROWD ONCE
AGAIN. PHEW! WHAT A
~~WONDERFUL~~ RELIEF. NOW
OFF TO ~~XXXXXXX~~
MEET MR X.

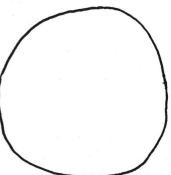

WHEN I GET UP IN THE MORNING
THERE IS MUCH TO BE DONE.
FIRST MY LIMBS MUST BE ATTATCHED
THIS IS FAIRLY EASY, OR HAS BEEN
MADE EASY BY CRAFTSMEN. ONCE
THIS IS DONE I MUST LOAD
MY BRAIN INTO MY SKULL. THE
BRAIN IS KEPT IN OIL TO KEEP
IT SMOOTH. NEXT I CHECK THE
INCUBATOR TO SEE IF ANY OF
THEM HAVE HATCHED OR COOKED.
AFTER THAT ALL THAT REMAINS
TO BE DONE IS TO HAVE MY
BREAKFAST (THOUGH I HAVE TO
CATCH IT FIRST OF COURSE).

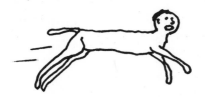

A DOG

A C.D. PLAYER

BONES

C.D.'s

KENNEL

SPECIAL HI-FI SHELF

WOOF

ROCK

CATS

VINYL

THE BLACKSMITH STARTED BY MAKING SHOES FOR HORSES.

THEN HE DECIDED TO MAKE COINS AND KEYS FOR OTHERS' HOUSES

THEN WAS PUT IN PRISON AND WAS FORCED TO MAKE BITS OF RAILWAY TRACK

THEN HE MADE A SWORD WITH WHICH HE ESCAPED FROM PRISON

THEN HE WENT BACK TO PRISON AND WAS FORCED TO MAKE CHAINS WHICH WERE PUT ON HIM WHILE HE MADE MORE RAILWAY TRACK.

THEN HE JUST MADE CROSSES AND STUFF THEN HE WAS KILLED WITH A SPEAR.

FREE GIFT

1.
2.
3.
4.
5.
6.
7.
8.
9.

WHICH ONE DO YOU WANT? THE MOBILE PHONE? EVERYONE ALWAYS WANTS THE MOBILE PHONE. NOBODY EVER WANTS THE HAIRY CABBAGE OR THE GORILLA. FEW PEOPLE EVER WANT THE SHAMROCK-THING, THEY OFTEN SEEM UNSURE OF WHAT IT ACTUALLY IS. THERE ARE A FEW WHO WANT THE FLAG FROM TIME TO TIME, THOUGH THERE'S ONLY BEEN ONE PERSON WHO WANTED THE TENTACLE (I THINK HE WAS A SAILOR). KIDS OFTEN WANT THE BALL AND SOME PEOPLE GO FOR THE RING, ESPECIALLY AT CHRISTMAS. PEOPLE SEEM TO WANT THE HAND NOW AND AGAIN, MORE OFTEN NOW THE FOOT ISN'T AVAILIABLE.

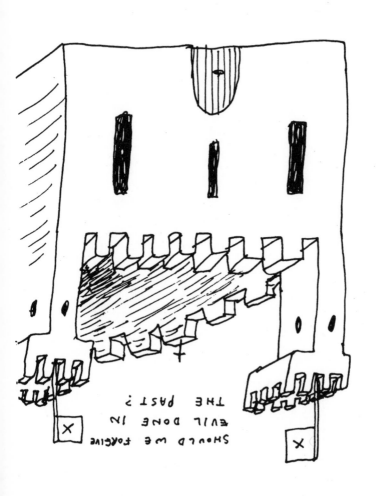

SHOULD WE FORGIVE
EVIL DONE IN
THE PAST?

LADDER USED FOR VIEWING
ATROCITY

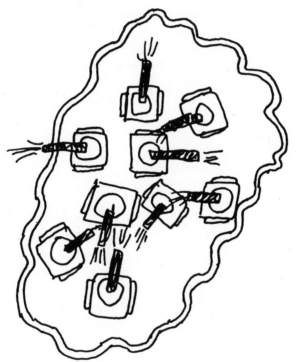

THE TANKS BECAME STRANDED
IN THE ENCLOSE AND STARTED
TO OPEN FIRE ON THEMSELVES

FAMILY PHOTOS
(TORN & DISCARDED)
LIVES RUINED
PETS LOST
HOUSES BURNED

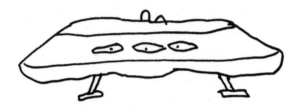

IF YOU TAKE YOUR EYE OFF THE
PEN FOR A ~~MERE~~ SECOND
THE DRAWING CAN CHANGE INTO
SOMETHING YOU NEVER MEANT

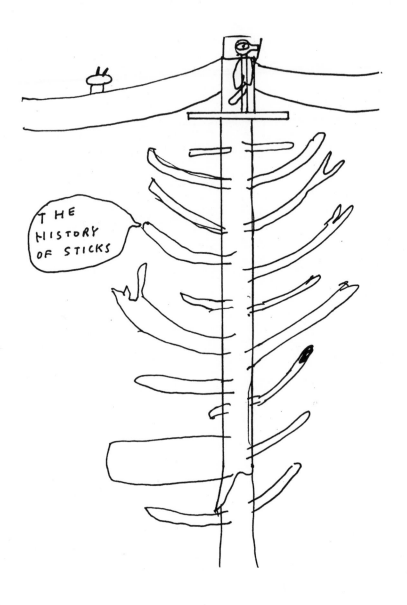

ILLUSTRATION

OUTSIDE THE TANK

BLUE SKY
CONVERSATION
COME + GO AT WILL
CHEESE SANDWICHES
 SINGING SONGS
DIRTY JOKES
EXUBERANT LAUGHTER

BARS OF CHOCOLATE
SKY T.V.
CREME EGGS
RADIO TIMES
HOT SHOWER
HANG GLIDING
M + M's

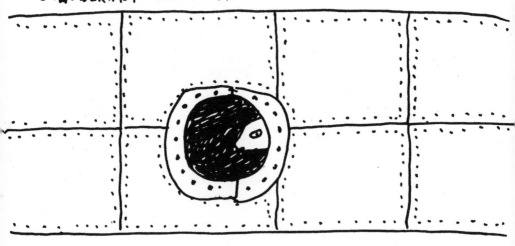

INSIDE THE DARK TANK

TINY SUBMARINES UP YOUR NOSE
DANGER

ATTACKED BY ADULTS

ATTACKED BY CHILDREN

THIS CAKE IS FOR YOU. IT'S YOUR BIRTH-DAY. YOU DESERVE IT SO STOP CRYING

ICECUBES

WILL MELT IN OVEN

S. AMERICAN 2-TOED RUMINANT

LLAMA

USED AS BEAST OF BURDEN

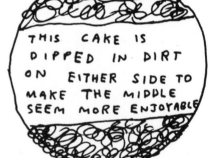

THIS CAKE IS DIPPED IN DIRT ON EITHER SIDE TO MAKE THE MIDDLE SEEM MORE ENJOYABLE

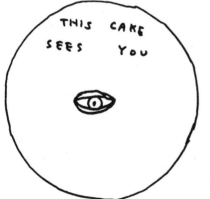

THIS CAKE SEES YOU

STRANGELY THIS CAKE DIVIDES EQUALLY, AMPLY ALWAYS WITH NO MATTER WHOEVER OR HOW MANY. YOU CAN EAT IT ALL AND STILL HAVE SOME LEFT.

THE END OF THE CIRCUS

ESCAPED MONKEY

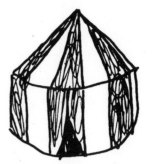

THE BIG TOP IS TOO SMALL

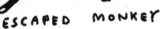

SCARY

A NET IS MADE FROM THE NET BENEATH THE TIGHTROPE + TRAPEZE

THE CLOWN WEARS A BLACK NOSE

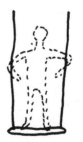

THE RING

THE GIANT PERFORMING MOUSE IS FOUND DEAD IN ITS CAGE. TONIGHTS SHOW IS CANCELLED

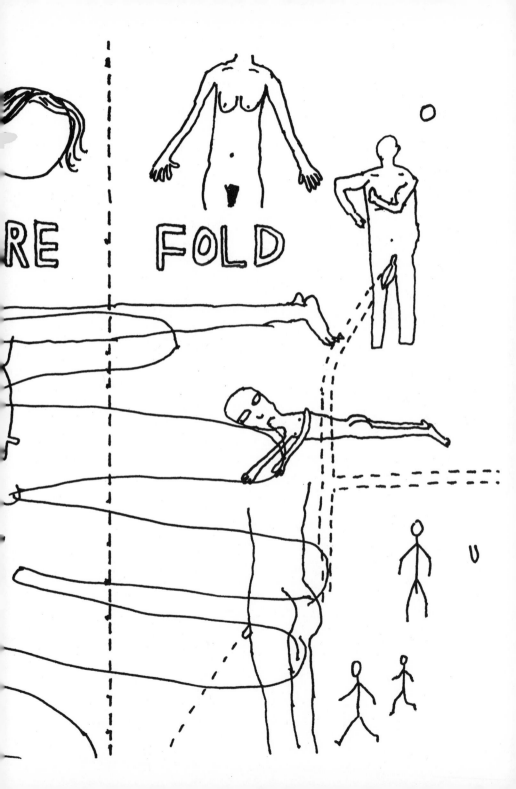

RE FOLD

DIFFERENT ASHTRAYS

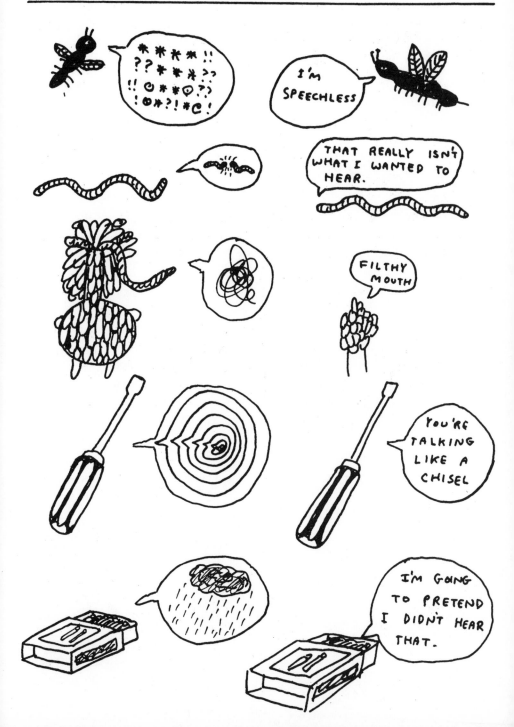

THE SEARCH FOR A WIFE OR HUSBAND SHOULD ALWAYS' START IN THE PUBLIC LIBRARY.....

PROCESSES

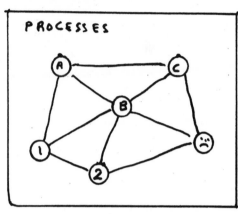

GONE FOR LUNCH

YOUTH HOSTEL

FROM THE TOP OF THE TALLEST TREE

GRAFFITI ISLAND

CONCLUSION

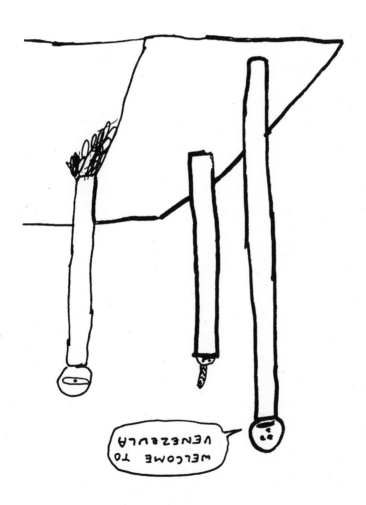

MAPS

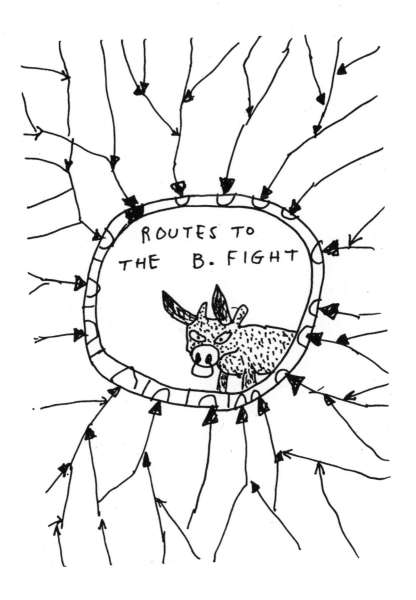

THE DUST JACKET

FOLDS

PICTURE OF THE AUTHOR

WORDS ABOUT AUTHOR

FRONT

(PICTURE)

SWEARWORD TITLE

SWEARWORD AUTHOR

SWEARWORD PUBLISHER

FOLDS
FOLDS

PUBLISHER AUTHOR TITLE

PUBLISHER DATE PRICE

BACK

PICTURE

SWEARWORD

SWEARWORD PUBLISHER NUMBER DATE PRICE

FOLDS

WORDS ABOUT THE BOOK

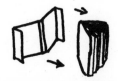

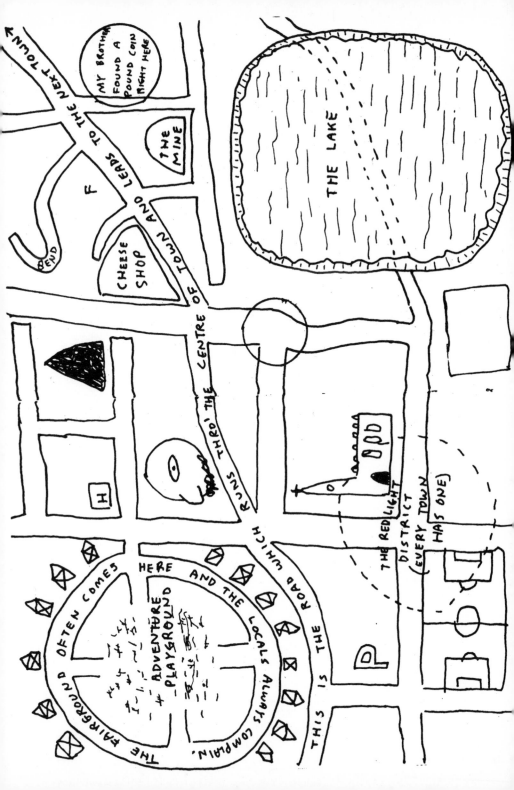

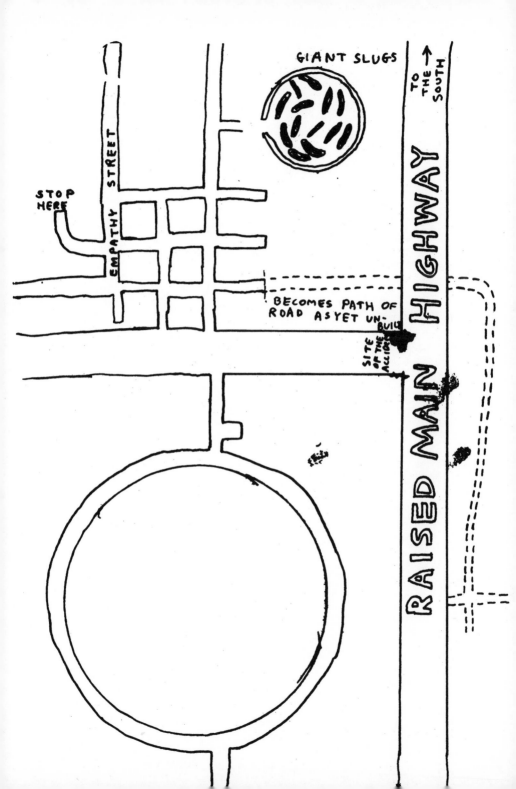

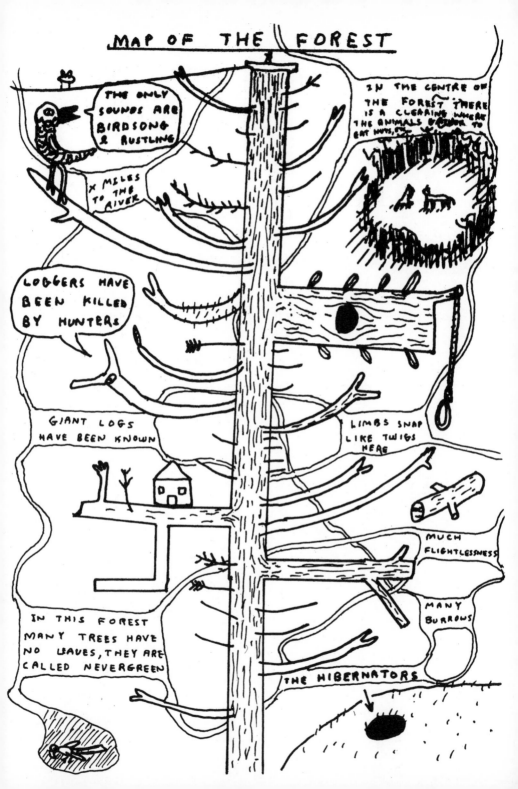

NATURE

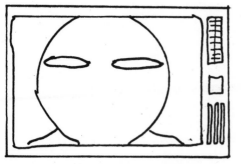

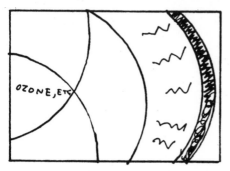

SOMETIMES THERE COMES A POINT WITH THINGS THAT YOU REALLY LIKE THAT YOU REALISE THAT EVERYTHING YOU LIKED ABOUT THAT THING, EVERYTHING YOU THOUGHT WAS GENIUS, WAS ARRIVED AT THRO' FLUKE, JUST AIMLESS CHANCE.

PROGRAMME   (APPENDIX II)

INITIALLY;

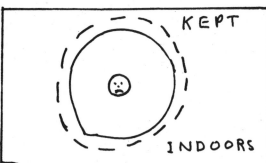

KEPT

INDOORS

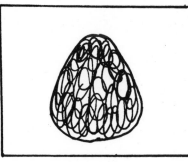

LOW-SCORING
BULLSEYE

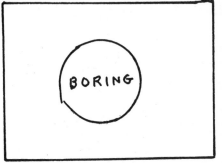

BORING

SQUIDS

MEN + BEASTS
AS SPECIMENS,
KEPT IN
SEPERATE TANKS.

THE CHARTS

BEFORE YOU LOOK AT
THE CHARTS YOU SHOULD
REALISE TWO THINGS ; FIRSTLY
THAT THEY ARE NOT AT ALL
ACCURATE AND SECONDLY THAT
IT'S ████ONLY POSSIBLE TO BE
CORRECT TO A CERTAIN EXTENT
IF THE ██████████ ██ ████
███████ ████ ████ ███ ███
IS ██ ███ ████ ████ ███ ████
IS.

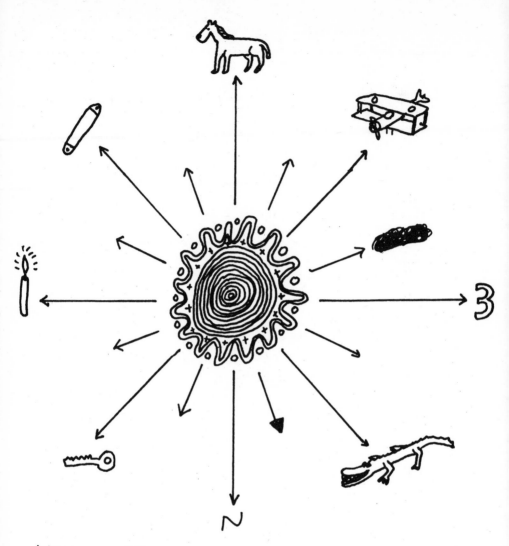

WHICH WAY IS THE PATTERN GOING TO MOVE?
BEARING IN MIND THAT IT HAS BEEN MOVING DUE
HORSE FOR THE LAST 10 YEARS WITHOUT SIGN OF
CHANGE THE ANSWER SEEMS OBVIOUS. HOWEVER
ANYLISTS HAVE NOTICED A VERY SLIGHT SHIFT
TOWARDS THE BIPLANE IN THE PAST COUPLE OF
YEARS SO IT SEEMS FEASIBLE THAT IN THE FUTURE
THE DIRECTION WILL BE HORSE - BIPLANE.
(BUT N.B., THIS IS A SECRET AT THE MOMENT)

CHART SUCCESS

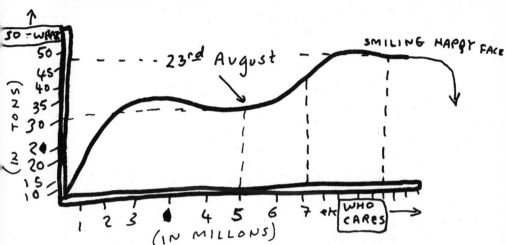

50 = WHAT

50
45
40
35
30

20
20
15
10

(IN TONS)

23rd August

SMILING HAPPY FACE

1 2 3 4 5 6 7 etc WHO CARES

(IN MILLONS)

HE HAD GRAND AND STUPID IDEAS WHICH ALWAYS CAME TO NOTHING HOWEVER THE WAY IN WHICH HE MAPPED THESE FAILURES IN FANCY CHARTS, GRAPHS, AND LISTS COMPILED AND BOUND IN HUGE SMASHING GREAT LEDGERS HAD MYSELF AND THE OTHER TRADESMEN IN AWE.

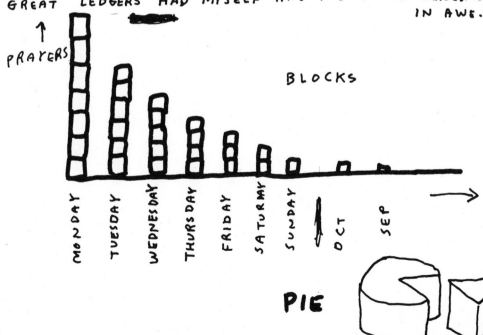

PRAYERS

BLOCKS

MONDAY TUESDAY WEDNESDAY THURSDAY FRIDAY SATURDAY SUNDAY OCT SEP

PIE

GAMES WON & LOST UNDER THE MICROSCOPE

USE OF FACTOR X

TYRE

10 YR

100 YR

WOODWORM

BEFORE   AFTER

ALCOHOLISM

1 WEEK

6 WEEK

LOST LOVE

START

FINISH

USE OF TALISMAN

TYRE

10 YR

100 YR

WOODWORM

BEFORE   AFTER

ALCOHOLISM

1 WEEK

6 WEEK

LOST LOVE

START

FINISH

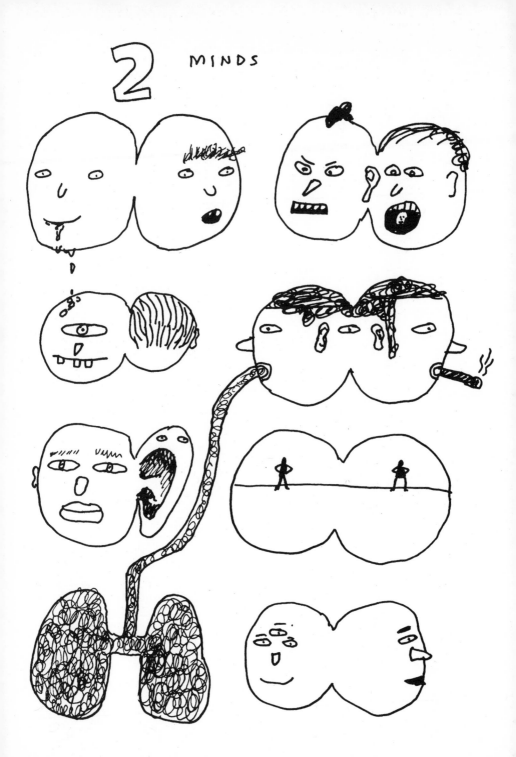

THE REASON WHY I HATE CHILDREN IS
CONTAINED IN THIS BOX;

THE REASON WHY I NEVER EVER REALLY
LIKED YOU IS CONTAINED IN THIS
ENVELOPE . . .

THE REASON WHY I'VE NEVER BEEN
ABLE TO CLEARLY EXPRESS MYSELF IN
THE COMPANY OF OTHERS IS BUNDLED
IN THIS ▬ SACK . . .

THE REASON WHY I DON'T GO TO CHURCH
ANYMORE IS CONTAINED IN THIS FLASK;

AND

(MAYBE LUCKILY) THE REASON WHY I AM
SAD, SHY AND SCARED HAS BEEN SNATCHED
FROM MY HAND AND SWALLOWED BY THE
HIDEOUS MYTHICAL BEAST PICTURED OVERLEAF.

6 FACTORS

1. PROBLEM PISSING (INCONTINENCE)
2. WHEN YOU WATCH A FILM AND YOU CONSTANTLY AWARE THAT THE CHARACTERS ARE NOT REAL, AND THEY ARE JUST ACTORS, ETC.
3. FAILURE TO UNDERSTAND SIMPLE WRITTEN INSTRUCTIONS.
4. THAT SHAPE WHERE YOU CAN'T TELL IF IT'S AN OLD GIRL OR YOUNG GIRL (DEPENDING ON HOW YOU LOOK AT IT)

5. A DAY IN JUNE AT THE COMMUNITY CENTRE WHEN THEY SHOW FILMS OF OLD HORSE RACES.

6. A CHANCE ENCOUNTER. WHICH WILL NEVER, COULD NEVER, HAPPEN AGAIN

QUIZ

T.V. OR ? MICROWAVE

ANSWERS:

NUMBER 1 IS A T.V.

NUMBER 2 IS A T.V.

NUMBER3 IS A T.V.

NUMBER4 IS A T.V.

NUMBER5 IS A T.V.

NUMBER6 IS A T.V.

NUMBER7 IS A T.V.

NUMBER 8 IS A T.V.

NUMBER 9 IS A T.V.

NUMBER 10 IS A T.V.

NUMBER 11 IS A T.V.

NUMBER 12 IS A T.V.

NUMBER 13 IS A T.V.

NUMBER 14 IS A T.V.

NUMBER 15 IS A BOX

NUMBER 16 IS A T.V.

FOOTN

1. THIS IS ALL SO WRONG, I'VE JUST GOT A BAD FEELING ABOUT THE WHOLE THING.
2. FRED ECLAIR AND GINGER BISCUIT
3. WE SHOULD HAVE USED A DICTIONARY BUT WE COULDN'T REALLY BE BOTHERED.
4. LEICESTER
5.

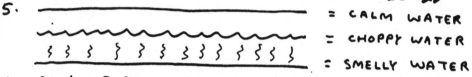

= CALM WATER
= CHOPPY WATER
= SMELLY WATER

6. DON'T FORGET TO PHONE YOUR MUM, SHE'S GETTING TIRED OF TALKING TO THE ANSWER PHONE.
7. HOW DID YOU GET THAT HUGE LUMP ON YOUR FOREHEAD?
8. I DON'T KNOW, I THINK I MUST HAVE GOT BITTEN
9. STAGES;

10. COTTAGE (CHEESE)
11. LONG AGO BEFORE THE CITY WAS BUILT, WHEN IT WAS ALL COUNTRY E.T.C., AT THE PLACE WHERE MY EX-GIRLFRIEND'S FLAT IS NOW ●, THERE WAS A LITTLE POND (RIGHT WHERE HER ROOM IS ━━) WHERE ANIMALS WOULD COME TO DRINK AND SWIM. EVENTUALLY THE POND DRIED UP (BECAUSE OF THE SUN OR SOMETHING) AND A HUGE PRICKLY BUSH GREW WHICH DID NOT BEAR ANY FRUIT. WHEN THE CITY WAS BUILT THE WORKMEN DUG UP THE BUSH WITH A DIGGER AND PUT IT IN A SKIP.
12. BURGLARY (IES)
13.

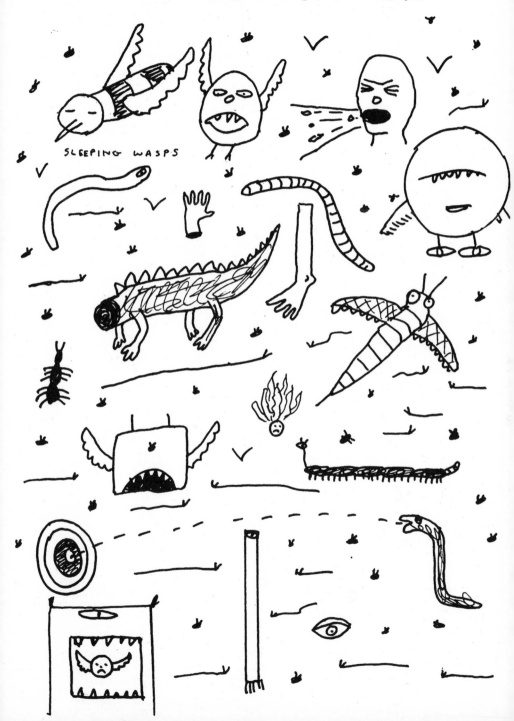

GLOSSARY OF TERMS (A. ANNOYING TAPS + FAUCETS)

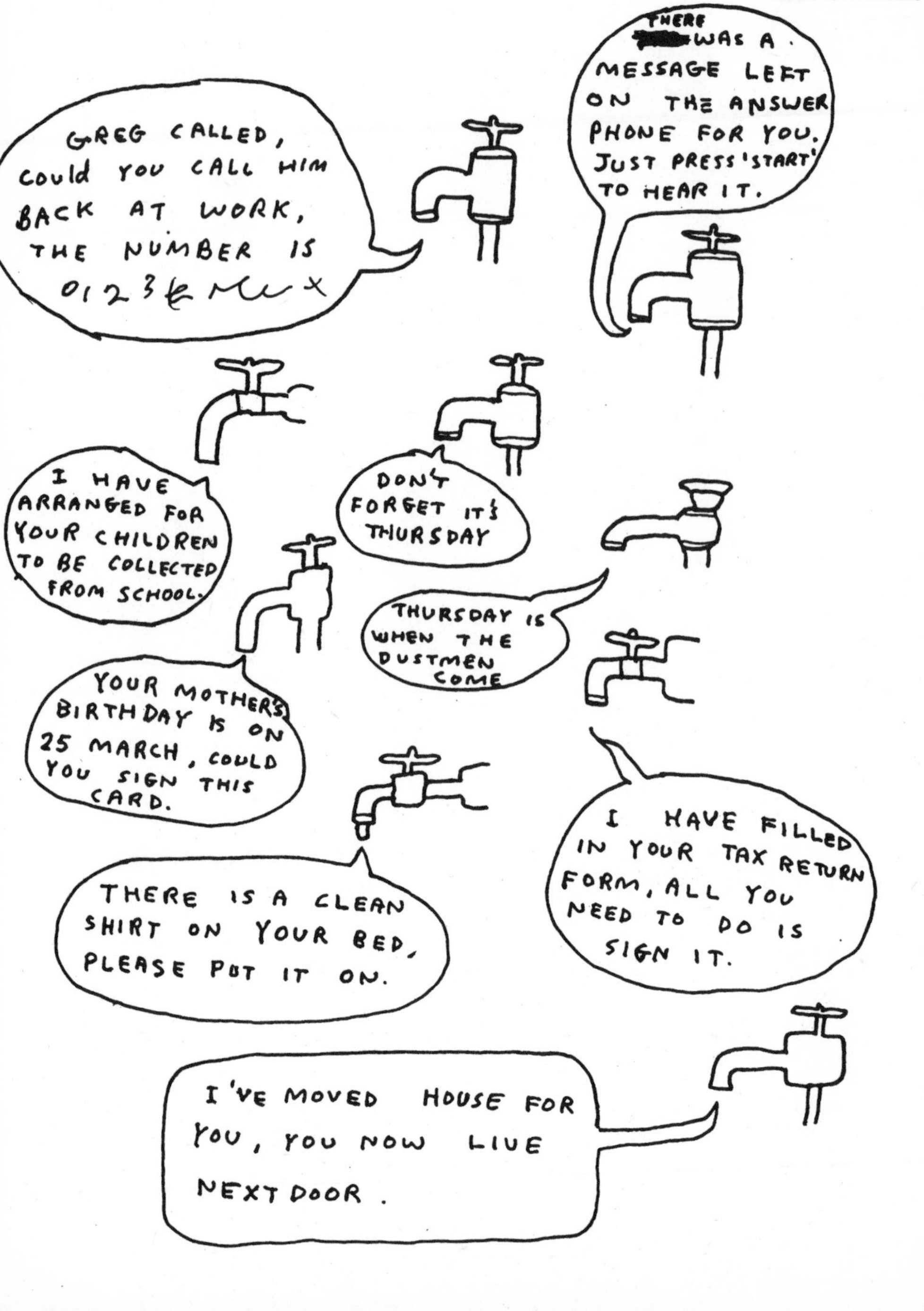

INDEX (P.T. 2)

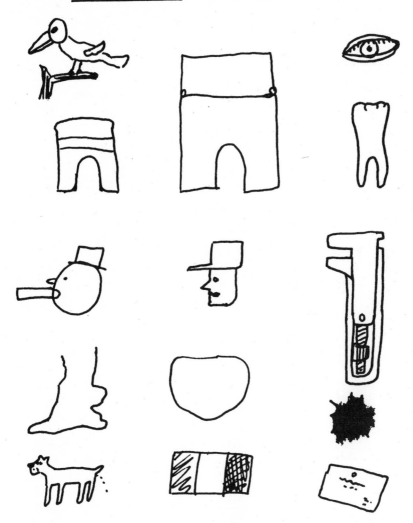

BIBLIOGRAPHY

BORROWED HISTORIES

THIS TREE

THAT MASK

THE BURIAL GROUND
(FENCED)

ALTERED CEREMONIES

UNOPENED CAN
OF BEER

CHIPS ~~WARM~~
(STILL WARM)

PEWTER TANKARD

CHANGED ADDRESSES

MUM

DAD

GRAN

FURTHER READING
(AS IF YOU NEEDED MORE TO DO)

- BUS TICKETS
- OLD NEWSPAPERS (YOU MIGHT HAVE MISSED SOMETHING THE FIRST TIME ROUND)
- GRAFFITI
- ~~PARRLIBTHTHHMTHETHTHH~~ (THIS WOULD JUST BE MISLEADING)
- TRAIN TIMETABLES
- FOUND LISTS, LETTERS.
- ALL THE LETTERS SHE WROTE TO YOU (READ THEM ALL OVER AGAIN)
- FORIEGN BOOKS, JOURNALS.
- CRICKET SCORES
- THE LAST LETTER SHE WROTE TO YOU (READ THIS ONE ESPECIALLY)
- SIGNS, BARCODES
- COMPUTER LANGAUGE (010101010 - YOU KNOW)
- THE LETTER FROM HER FAMILY WRITTEN AFTER THE FIRST ATTEMPT.
- OTHER PEOPLES' RECEIPTS
- OTHER PEOPLES' BANK STATEMENTS
- OTHER PEOPLES' CRIMINAL RECORDS
- L.P. COVERS
- CAR MAINTENENCE MANUALS
- THE NOTE SHE TRIED TO SCRATCH INTO THE DASHBOARD.
- THE MINDS OF YOUR ENEMIES
- PORNO MAGS
- THE BOX THAT THE STEREO CAME IN
- SWEARWORDS WRITTEN IN THE DIRT ON THE SIDE OF THE BUS.

BUILDING

BACK IN THE EARLY DAYS
THEY WERE ALL DEAD KEEN
TO BUILD THINGS ALL OVER
THE PLACE. THEY DIDN'T
KNOW WHAT THEY WERE
UP TO REALLY BUT SOME
OF THE THINGS THEY DID
WE O.K. - ANYWAY WE'RE
NOT ALLOWED TO KNOCK THEM DOWN

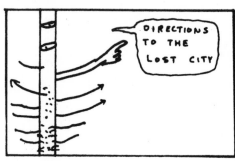

IT'S ALWAYS A SHAME WHEN
BEAUTIFUL THINGS HAVE
TO BE DESTROYED.

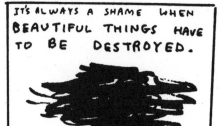

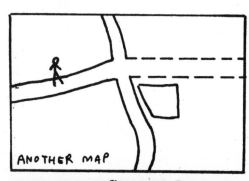

ANOTHER MAP

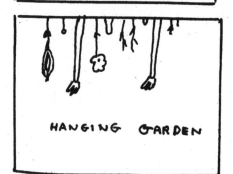

HANGING GARDEN

PROGRAMME {APPENDIX V}

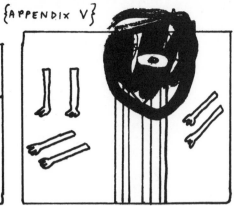

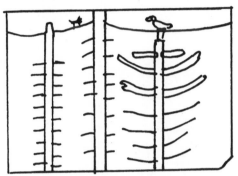

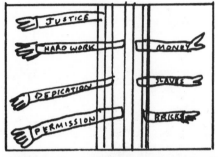

JUSTICE
HARD WORK
DEDICATION
PERMISSION
MONEY
SLAVES
BRICKS

WE INTERFERE WITH YOUR T.V.

GOOD THINGS	BAD THINGS
CEMENT	RAIN
	WOODPECKERS
	SPIT
	FIRE
	THE WRECKERS
	A.M. BOOZING
	THEFT
	CHAOS
	FLU

THEY LIVE IN THIS HOLE AND WE'LL NEVER GET THEM OUT.

CONTRIBUTORS

TO THIS EDITION

'SEÑOR'   WAYNE P.   MR. W.   THE ▬

MIKE W.   B. SMITH   E. WATSON

CARROT   DAWN TRADER

JERRY   J. DILKS   THE XXX

ACKNOWLEDGEMENTS

HIS SHOW WAS NO GOOD BECAUSE

INTESTINES TAKEN OUT OF THE BODY AND MADE TO LOOK LIKE FLOWERS — BORING

HEADS ON SPIKES ON THE CITY WALLS — OH PLEASE!, IT'S SO SIXTH-FORM.

BOILING OIL POURED DOWN FROM THE RAMPARTS ONTO HIS ENEMIES — SO SILLY.

PUBLIC HANGING — HE'S OBVIOUSLY DESPERATE TO PLEASE ███ ████.

HUMAN LIMBS SEVERED AND SEWN ON TO HORSES. — BAD MOVE.

A FIRE-BREATHING DRAGON - ENTERTAINING FOR THE KIDDIES MAYBE.

THE DEAD MADE TO WALK THRO' MAGIC — SEEN IT BEFORE.

SMALL, DELICATE MODELS OF SHIPS, E.T.C. STAMPED ON, SMASHED, RUINED.

— NOW THIS IS PRETTY GOOD.

THE PUBLISHER'S IMPRINT

THE PUBLISHER'S IMPRINT AS IT APPEARS
HERE, PROUD, EVOKING HERALDIC MYTH &
LEGEND WAS PREVIOUSLY ABSENT
DUE TO OVERSIGHT. IT SHOULD REALLY BE
IN COLOUR, ESPECIALLY THE PARROT HEAD
AND THE EYE.

EPILOGUE

HOW?, TELL ME HOW WHEN
I HAVE REMOVED THE
CARTRIDGE FROM THIS PEN
DOES IT K

<u>ON THE COVER</u> :

BRONZE STATUETTE OF A COCONUT
ETRUSCAN , 5TH C. , B.C.
H . 25.9 CM .

NEW WRITING SERIES

ERR
David Shrigley
Published and distributed by Book Works
19 Hollywell Row, London EC2A 4JB
www.bookworks.org.uk

First edition 1996
Second edition 1998
Third edition 2000
Fourth edition 2002
Fifth edition 2004
Sixth edition 2005
Seventh Edition 2006

ISBN 10: 1 870699 22 X
ISBN 13: 978 1 870699 22 8

New Writing Series
Editors: Michael Bracewell and Jane Rolo

Design by Rose-Innes Associates
Printed by Aldgate Press, London